THE MYSTERY OF

The Empty Tomb

The Story of Jesus

A long time ago, something mysterious happened…

In a city called Jerusalem, a very bad man called Barabbas was sitting in prison awaiting his punishment — death!

All of a sudden, out of nowhere, he was told he could go free! A man who had done nothing wrong was going to take the place of Barabbas. This man would die on a cross.

Why was this happening? It was a mystery…

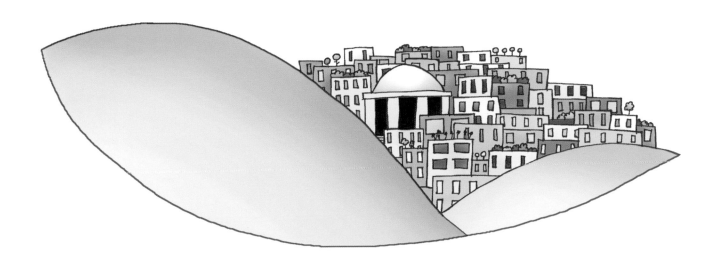

Jesus was the man who was going to take the place of Barabbas. Jesus had never done anything wrong. He made sick people better and told everyone about God. Jesus said that he was the King that God had promised, God's Son. But the important leaders did not like that. They did not want him to be their king. They wanted him to be killed.

When Pilate, the Roman ruler, met Jesus he knew that Jesus was innocent. He said to the leaders that he would set one prisoner free for them. "Would you like Jesus to go free?" he asked.

"No!" they said. "We want Barabbas!" (the bad man)

Pilate was shocked. "What about Jesus?" he asked.

"Kill him on a cross." they shouted.

Because God made and loved everybody in the world,
he had told us that we should love and obey him,
or he would have to punish us. But we did not listen.
We have not loved him and it makes him very sad.

The punishment God would give was death. This may
sound very bad news and make you sad…but God
made an amazing rescue plan.

God sent Jesus to be our Saviour and die for us. Jesus was taking God's punishment that we deserved. God's people could now be forgiven.

Jesus took the punishment for all the wrong things that we have ever done, said or thought.

Jesus the rescuer offers to set us free, just like Barabbas the bad man was set free.

And that was the mystery of the cross — a big swap!

But this amazing story doesn't stop here! Jesus had
promised his friends that he wouldn't stay dead.
He said he would come back to life after three days.
Would he really? They had to wait and see...

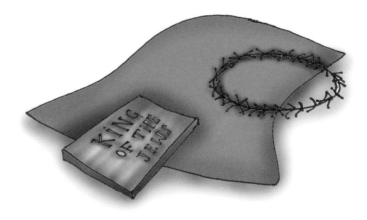

You can find this true story in the Bible — Matthew 27v11-54.

It was very early on Sunday morning and a small group of women crept through the garden. They had come to visit Jesus' grave. They were very scared.

They had sweet-smelling spices to put on the body. But there were two big problems…

"How are we going to get in?" they asked.

"The grave will be closed with a huge, heavy stone." said one of the women.

"How will we move it?" said another.

The women were also worried about the scary soldiers guarding the tomb. Maybe the soldiers wouldn't let them care for Jesus' body.

Jesus had said that God would bring him back to life again. That is why the Roman soldiers were at the tomb. They wanted to make sure nobody stole Jesus to trick people into thinking he was alive.

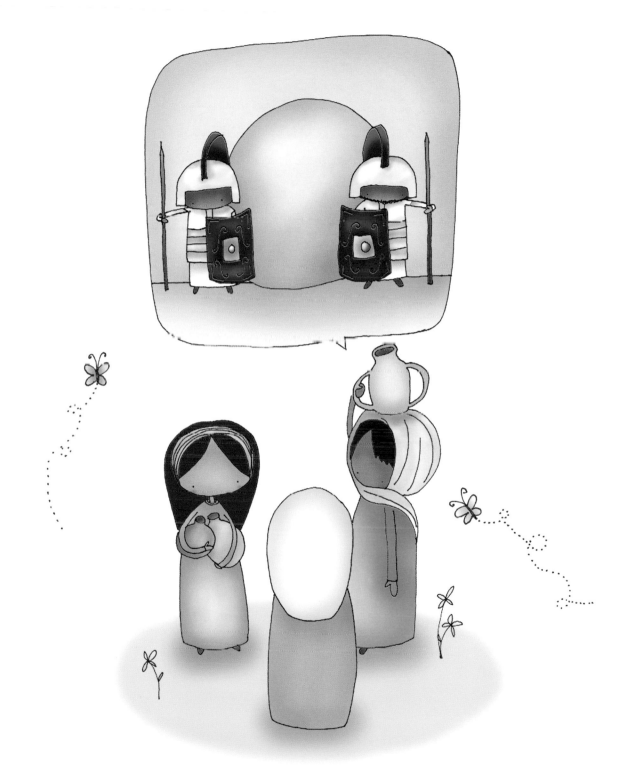

When the women got to the tomb, something mysterious happened. The earth shook and an angel rolled the huge stone away. The soldiers were so scared that they fell over! The women were scared too!

Angels are God's messengers and shine very brightly and look awesome. Perhaps that is because they spend time close to God, who is so perfect and powerful.

The angel told them not to be afraid. He said, "Jesus is not here, he is alive, just like he said. Look at the empty tomb, then go and tell his friends."

The women ran to find Jesus' friends. Peter and John came running to see what had happened. John was a faster runner than Peter and got there first.

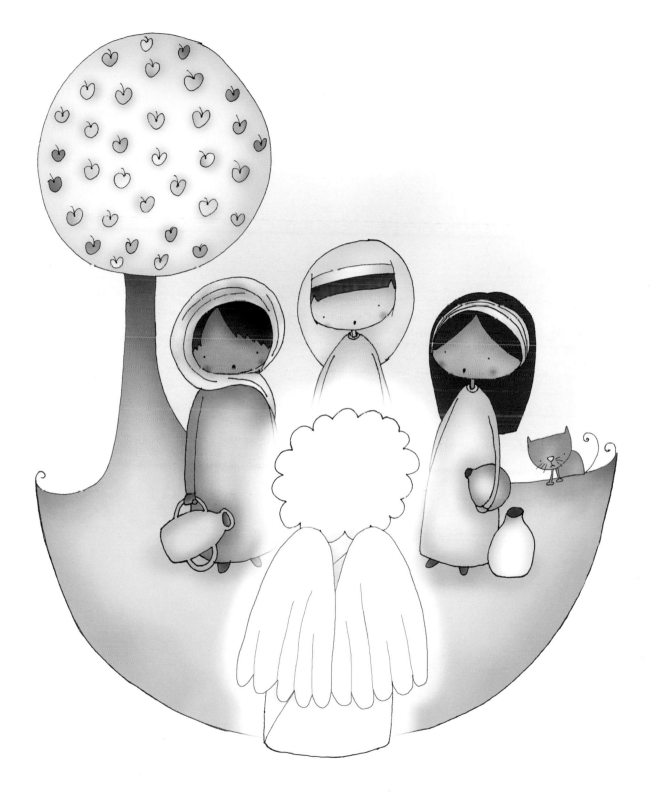

John stopped when he got to the tomb and peeped inside. Peter ran past him and went inside the tomb. The tomb was empty. They both saw the cloth that the body had been wrapped in, but no body. They went away wondering what had happened.

Jesus' body had gone. It could not have been stolen because the soldiers were guarding it. Where was it?

Was the angel right? Had Jesus really come back to life? He said that he would. But dead people do not come to life again, do they?

It was all very mysterious.

Mary stood outside the tomb crying. She loved Jesus and did not know where his body had gone. She took another look into the tomb.

This time she saw two angels. They asked her why she was crying.

"I don't know where they have taken my Lord's body," she said. Then she turned round. There was a man behind her.

"Why are you crying?" he asked. "Who are you looking for?"

"Have you moved the body?" she asked.

"Mary," said the man.

It was Jesus!

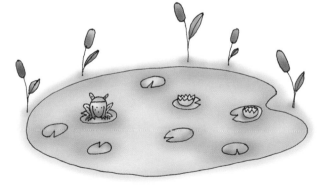

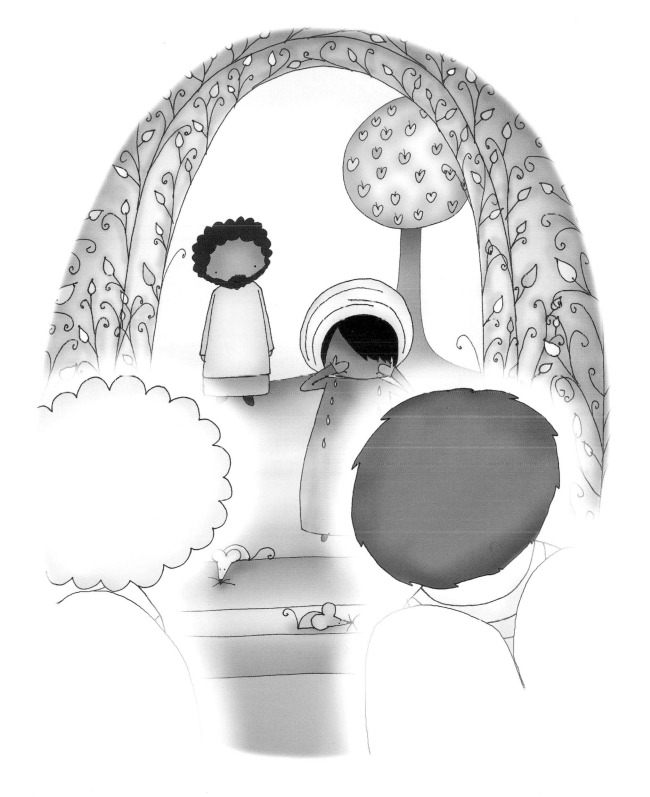

Mary was so surprised and happy. She wanted to hold on tightly to him forever. The body hadn't been stolen. The body hadn't disappeared. The mystery was solved. Jesus was alive!

Jesus gave her a special job to do. He wanted her to tell all her friends that he was alive. Mary was so happy to have such good news to tell people. Jesus was so powerful he was even stronger than death.

Everything that Jesus said would happen, did happen. Jesus is alive today and we celebrate that he died and came alive again at Easter. We can be his friends just like Mary, Peter and John.

You can find this true story in the Bible — Matthew 28v1-10

For Grace, Reuben, James, Eloise and Catherine

The Mystery of the Empty Tomb

Text and Illustrations© 2013. Cassie Martin and Jenny Brake.

Published by 10Publishing, a division of 10ofThose Limited.

ISBN 9781909611016

Design and Typeset by: Diane Bainbridge.

10Publishing, a division of 10ofthose.com

Unit C, Tomlinson Road, Leyland, PR25 2DY, England

Email: info@10ofthose.com   Website: www.10ofthose.com